FREE FALL

FOR KIM

Thanks to Matthew and Daniel

ISBN 0-590-45983-X

12 11 10 9 8 7 6 5 4 3 2 1   2 3 4 5 6 7/9

Printed in the U.S.A.   08

First Scholastic printing, September 1992

DAVID WIESNER

FREE FALL

SCHOLASTIC INC.

NEW YORK TORONTO LONDON AUCKLAND SYDNEY

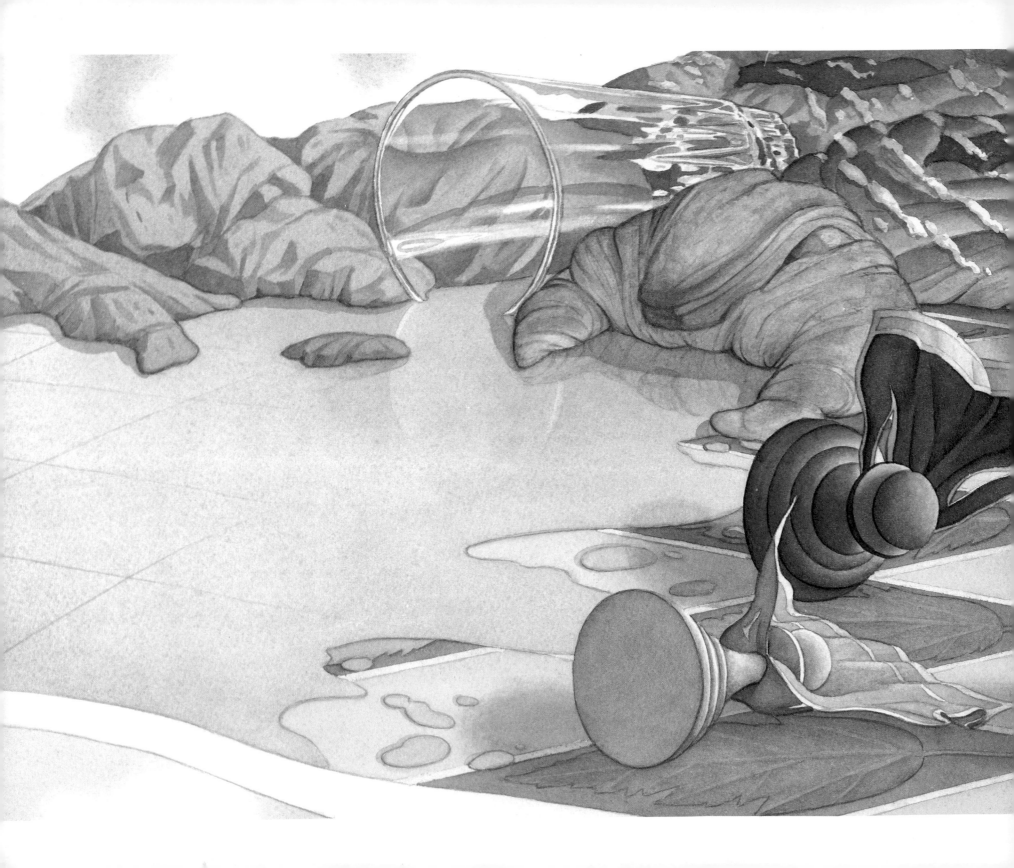